THE NORTH AMERICAN
BIGHORN SHEEP

OTHER BOOKS BY MARY ADRIAN

THE INDIAN HORSE MYSTERY
THE MYSTERY OF THE DINOSAUR BONES
THE SKIN DIVING MYSTERY
THE MYSTERY OF THE NIGHT EXPLORERS
THE RARE STAMP MYSTERY
THE FOX HOLLOW MYSTERY
JONATHAN CROW, DETECTIVE
THE URANIUM MYSTERY
REFUGEE HERO

THE PRESERVE OUR WILDLIFE SERIES

THE AMERICAN EAGLE
THE AMERICAN MUSTANG
THE NORTH AMERICAN WOLF
Hastings House

GARDEN SPIDER
HONEYBEE
FIDDLER CRAB
GRAY SQUIRREL
Holiday House

THE FIREHOUSE MYSTERY
THE TUGBOAT MYSTERY
Houghton Mifflin Company

THE HIDDEN SPRING MYSTERY
THE JUNIOR SHERIFF MYSTERY
Farrar, Straus & Giroux

PRESERVE OUR WILDLIFE SERIES

THE
NORTH
AMERICAN
BIGHORN
SHEEP

BY MARY ADRIAN

Illustrated by

Genevieve Vaughan-Jackson

HASTINGS HOUSE • PUBLISHERS

NEW YORK

May I take this opportunity to express my appreciation to Dr. Helmut K. Buechner, Head of the Department of Ecology of the Smithsonian Institution at Washington, D.C., for his kindness in reading the manuscript for scientific accuracy and for the information obtained from his monograph,* "The Bighorn Sheep in the United States."

MARY ADRIAN

---

* Wildlife Monographs, a Publication of the Wildlife Society, May, 1960, No. 4.

Published simultaneously in Canada by Saunders of Toronto, Ltd. Toronto 2B.

Library of Congress Catalog Card Number 66-20538

Printed in the United States of America

FOREWORD

Scientists believe that wild sheep crossed from Siberia to Alaska on the Bering land bridge about three hundred thousand years ago, during the middle of the Ice Age. With them came other animals, including the bison or buffalo, the bear, and the elk.

When large icecaps pushed down from the north, the wild sheep moved to ice-free areas, but many of the other animals were killed by the glaciers. Some wild sheep traveled to the rugged mountains of our southwestern states. Others did not go that far. Gradually they became two separate species according to where they lived.

Ovis canadensis is the Latin name for the bighorn

sheep. They are heavy-bodied animals, and the rams have massive horns. Their coats are not wolly like those of our domestic sheep, but are hairy like the deer's. They vary in color from the dark grayish-brown of the bighorns that live in the rugged Rocky Mountain country to the pale buffy dress of those in the high desert areas from northern Mexico to southern Canada.

Ovis dalli are the northern wild sheep. They are somewhat smaller, and the rams' horns are not as large. Their coats vary in color from the white dress of the Dall sheep to the brownish-black of the Stone Sheep. They exist mostly in Alaska and parts of the Yukon.

Years ago the Indians hunted wild sheep with spears, and bows and arrows. Since bighorns were abundant in the valleys in winter when they came down from their mountain ranges for food, the Indians killed them for meat and used their hides for clothing and moccasins.

Before the white man came to the West, almost two million bighorn sheep lived in the United States. At present only about twenty thousand remain, according to Dr. Buechner's monograph on bighorn sheep. The largest drop in population took place in the last half of the nineteenth century. The white man killed great numbers of bighorns not only for their meat and large horns but because he wanted their feeding areas for his own cattle and sheep. Band after band of bighorns disappeared from the high mountain ranges. The lambs died of starvation and disease because of lack of food in winter. In 1930 there were only three hundred desert bighorn sheep left in Nevada.

Fortunately, in 1936, by order of Franklin D. Roosevelt, President of the United States, two million acres of mountainous desert country in Nevada were set aside for bighorn sheep. This refuge is called the Desert Game Range. In 1939 two other smaller refuges, the Kofa and Cabeza Prieta Game Ranges, were also set aside in southern Arizona.

Today hunting is allowed on the Desert Game Range. Local gunners forced the opening of the refuge to public shooting of bighorn sheep, because their large horns make excellent trophies in the world of sport. This seems unfortunate. Since this refuge was originally set aside for the protection of bighorns, it should remain as such. In this way all people will have the opportunity of seeing them in their natural habitat, and the species will be preserved.

Poachers also have become a problem on the Desert Game Range. These men break the law by killing bighorn sheep out of hunting season. With the perfection of telescope sights on rifles, this is easy to do. Workers at the refuge are few in number and cannot track down all the poachers on the large area of land. As a result too many desert bighorn sheep are being killed on the refuge to maintain a permanent population.

Recently the Bureau of Reclamation, which was established to restore wasted land to usefulness, has asked for a dam to be built in Grand Canyon National Park.

Dams are one of the sources of inexpensive electric power, but certainly there are other places in our country where they can be built. Not only would a dam ruin the beautiful Grand Canyon, but much of the land where the desert bighorns live would be flooded.

Rocky Mountain bighorn sheep are given protection in Glacier and Yellowstone National Parks. They are also unmolested in Banff and Jasper National Parks in Canada. But they have been driven from many ranges in their natural home, the Rocky Mountains. In Montana, Wyoming, and Colorado ranchers inhabit many of the valleys, and their cattle graze on the grass and other vegetation there. The lower slopes are also used for feeding, which means that bighorn sheep are fast disappearing from their original mountain habitat.

Just as their ancestors long ago weathered the upheaval of the Ice Age when other animals perished, our bighorn sheep have endured many hardships, such as extreme cold and little food. But they are different from some wild creatures that have managed to adapt to a life near people. They can exist only in wilderness country.

For this reason the remaining bighorns of North America need more refuges where food is abundant and where hunters cannot kill them for their magnificent horns. Otherwise they will not survive, and a truly beautiful American animal will become extinct.

Salem, Oregon

MARY ADRIAN

THE NORTH AMERICAN
BIGHORN SHEEP

1

BOW AND ARROW

It was wintertime, many years ago. Fresh snow had fallen on the Rocky Mountain peaks in Wyoming. Down in the valley the ground was covered with a thick white blanket. When the sun came out the trees and shrubs sparkled like crystals and the frozen river shone like silver.

In November a band of ten Rocky Mountain bighorn sheep had come down from the high slopes for food. They were looking for grass and low shrubs to eat along the river bank. They were all rams—males with large curving horns, grayish-brown coats, and rumps as white as the snow.

Other flocks of bighorn sheep had left their high summer grazing grounds for the valley. Some of these were ewes—female sheep with small spiked horns. Their youngsters, almost full grown, tagged along with them.

The band of ten male bighorns pawed with their hoofs to uncover some grass, but the recent snowfall made it hard to find. So they set out for a dwarf willow thicket whose buds and twigs tasted fairly good in winter when they could find nothing else.

The breath from their nostrils steamed in the cold air as the bighorns walked single file along the river bank, following the ram with the largest horns. He acted as their leader and frequently sniffed the air for wolves, mountain lions, and Indians.

It was not long before a pine squirrel poked his head out of a hollow in a fir tree and chattered at the wild sheep going by. Unlike some animals who hibernate or sleep through the winter, the pine squirrel is very active and stays in a

tree hole only during storms and bitter cold weather. Now the sun shining on his side of the tree made this one frisky. His voice sounded unusually loud in the stillness of the valley, and all the bighorns looked up at him. Then they continued on their way.

13

Soon a bird with broad wings flew silently over their heads. It was a snowy owl, who is different from most owls because he hunts in the daytime. He had just caught sight of a white-tailed jackrabbit near a stump.

With the speed of a lightning bolt, the owl swooped down, seized the rabbit in his great

talons, and flew to a nearby tree to eat his catch. Shifting on the branch to make himself comfortable, he sent down a shower of snow on two bighorns. They shook themselves from their horns to their rumps and fell into line at the end of the procession.

Presently the band of wild sheep came to buffalo tracks—large hoof marks that zigzagged ahead. They followed them a short way until the tracks trailed to the left. Then the flock walked alongside the footprints of a red fox and a long-tailed weasel.

The tracks of these two animals suddenly ended near a big log. Blood and chunks of white fur lay on the snow where the fox had caught his prey. The weasel's change from a summer-brown coat to winter white had not saved his life. On the other side of the log, the fox's tracks went on alone.

The bighorns, who had often seen their winter neighbors kill for food when they were hungry, did not stop to examine the telltale evidence.

First the leader and then the rest of the band
jumped over the log and moved along toward
the willow thicket. They had as yet no hint that
two Indians were hiding there.

The Indians knew well the eating habits of
the Rocky Mountain bighorns, and since there
were so many of the sheep in the valley in winter, they hunted them for food. Now, with bows
and arrows ready, they waited for this band to
arrive.

The procession of wild sheep walked steadily

16

forward, drawing closer to the thicket. Soon they were only a few hundred feet away.

The Indians did not move. They wanted the bighorns to start nibbling on the willow twigs. Then it would be easier to shoot them.

One minute, two minutes went by. Now the bighorns were only a hundred feet from the thicket, but they could not see the Indians, nor could they catch their scent because of the wind direction.

Just then a black-billed magpie flew over the dwarf willows and caught sight of the two crouched figures. His black and white feathers gleamed in the sunlight as he swooped and screamed above the Indians' hiding place.

Often he screamed when there was no need for it, but right now his excited cries made the bighorns stop dead in their tracks. With heads up they looked and sniffed around them, but they still could scent no danger.

The magpie circled and screamed some more, making such a racket that the Indians decided

17

not to wait any longer. As they crept forward, the leader of the bighorns saw them. Instantly he snorted an alarm and turned to run in the opposite direction. The others immediately followed, their white rumps bouncing over the snow.

A second later the Indians took aim, and two
arrows sped through the air. One missed a bighorn by a few inches. The other arrow struck
the side of the leader near his heart. Without
making a sound the animal fell to the ground.

The Indians lost no time in dressing the game in the snow. As they started back to camp with the meat, the magpie flew down and walked around the remains of the dead sheep with short, jerky steps. Then, being a scavenger, he commenced to eat.

Soon another magpie arrived and was quickly followed by several more. They pushed and squawked to get their share until a coyote came dashing up. Instantly the magpies scattered and took to the air. Later they returned, but the coyote had left little for them to eat.

2

MANY YEARS LATER

Spring had come to the Rocky Mountains in Wyoming. Grass sprouted on the high slopes, and flowers bloomed in the little meadows.

Suddenly the warmness of the day was broken by a sharp wind blowing. Black clouds moved swiftly in the sky. They rushed against each other, and presently lightning danced in the darkened heavens. Then came crashes of thunder, each one sounding louder than the one before. Soon the storm broke, and cold rain mixed with snow fell in torrents.

While the storm raged, a Rocky Mountain bighorn sheep waited for her lamb to be born. She was standing on a high ledge above timberline where there were no trees.

Her ancestors had always gone to high sheltered places to bear their young, safe from wolves. Now the ewe did not have to worry about wolves, since the ranchers in the valleys had destroyed them to protect their livestock. Her greatest fear was the hunters who roamed the mountains gunning down wild sheep because they were good eating, and the rams' horns made wonderful trophies.

In a little while the dark clouds rolled by, and the sun shone on the peaks and rugged slopes. By this time the ewe's lamb had come into the world on the high ledge—a trembling little youngster with a mouse-colored coat. The mother licked him until he was dry. Then she bleated for him to get up.

Young Bighorn needed no further coaxing. He was hungry. Gradually he managed to stand up on his wobbly legs. He stretched his neck and had his first taste of milk from his mother.

She waited for him to finish. After that she left the nursery, snatched a few bites of grass, and came back to keep on the lookout for danger.

Soon she saw a red-tailed hawk circling on its broad wings overhead. It was a large bird, but since it hunted only small animals, the mother showed no alarm.

A short while later, though, she became tense. "Bang! Bang! Bang!" echoed in the mountains. A hunter was shooting at some sort of game.

For the next few moments all was still. Then more shots rang out. With each one the mother drew closer to Bighorn. The lamb, feeling the warmth of her body, dozed off. He was still sleeping when a golden eagle appeared in the sky and dropped low to find a perch for the night.

The next morning Bighorn was awake at daybreak. His mother nursed him frequently with feedings that lasted about three minutes. In a little while the sun began to rise. Bighorn looked out from the high ledge and watched the huge reddish ball move slowly above the snow-capped peaks. His gaze also took in the rocky points jutting up into the sky like towers. Then he went to the edge of the ledge and stared down at the rolling slopes and the valley far below. But not once during the day did he leave the nursery, and after a week had gone by, he was still there.

Now his mother felt that he was strong enough to travel with her while she roamed the mountains for food. One morning after nursing Bighorn, she bleated for him to follow her.

Sniffing the cool air, he walked behind her along the trail down a steep cliff face. The path was so narrow in places that his mother's side rubbed against the cliff wall. Bighorn watched her closely, jumping just as she did from rock to rock, gripping them with the cushioned suction

cups on his black hoofs. He even leaped from one tiny ledge to another, showing more courage than most young animals do when they leave their nurseries. Usually their mothers have to coax them.

Finally Bighorn found himself at the bottom of the cliff. He ran ahead, but a bleating call from his mother quickly brought him back. Obediently he scampered alongside her until they came to a wide, open area partly surrounded with shrubs and brush. Grass, plants, and alpine flowers were growing there. While his mother browsed, Bighorn investigated a bed of purple lupines, nibbling on some of the flowers, until a

bee buzzed in front of his nose and made him draw away.

Then Bighorn heard his mother bleat in alarm. She had seen a hunter coming up over the ridge. Quick as a flash the ewe turned and started to run. Bighorn bounced along close at her heels.

As they came to the end of the small clearing, the hunter caught sight of them. He fired quickly, but his bullet whizzed by the mother and her lamb. At once she veered to the side and dashed down a slope. Bighorn raced after her.

At the bottom they came to a heap of rocks, all shapes and sizes. There the ewe stopped and so did Bighorn. He imitated his mother and froze, standing as still as a statue.

A few moments later the hunter looked down
the slope, but he could not see the ewe and her
lamb because their dark grayish-brown coats
blended in with the color of the rocks. Puzzled,
he walked away.

The ewe waited until it was safe to leave. Then
cautiously she led Bighorn to another green area
filled with flowers.

3

THE MEADOW

The next day Bighorn started on a second journey with his mother. She had found some fresh tracks of other wild sheep and was eager to follow them. Down a rocky slope and through a small field she went with her lamb scampering after her.

Suddenly Bighorn stopped to stare at a rather large plump animal sitting on a rock. This was his first sight of a hoary marmot, with its short legs and its silver-gray fur peppered with black. The marmot looked at Bighorn and then turned away to gaze out at the vast open space before him. A second later he whistled excitedly.

Instantly the ewe stopped in alarm, and Bighorn ran close to her side. The marmot kept on whistling. He and others of his kind spend a lot of time watching for enemies and letting other wild creatures know of danger. Now he was warning a pika, who is also called a cony or rock rabbit. She had a grayish-brown coat, small round ears, and hardly any tail — and she was choice meat for the red-tailed hawk flying overhead.

In a flash the pika hopped to safety down a hole in a rock slide where she lived. The marmot continued his vigil. And the ewe and Bighorn walked along, still following the hoof marks of other wild sheep.

It was not long before the tracks led them to a high mountain meadow where five ewes were eating grass. They paid no attention to their youngsters playing close by, because an old ewe was standing guard and looking for danger.

Bighorn immediately dashed up to the lambs to join in their fun. He chased a female round and round a big boulder until she stopped and switched her tail in a friendly way. Bighorn was

29

ready to play some more with her, but just then another lamb rushed up and butted him on the rump.

Bighorn swung around and returned the bump. Then he and the lamb cracked their heads together; but it all seemed to be in fun, for they scampered off side by side. In a little while they came back and joined in what appeared to be a game with the other lambs. One youngster was standing on a large flat rock in the meadow and another lamb was trying to push him off. He could not do it. So the next lamb shoved for all she was worth. Still the male stayed on the rock.

Suddenly Bighorn rushed up. He pushed so hard that the lamb slid off into the grass.

After that three more youngsters stood on the rock, but not one of them was able to remain there very long.

Now it was Bighorn's turn. He planted his feet firmly on the platform and signaled by shaking his head that he was ready.

First one lamb and then another tried to shove

him off. Bighorn moved a little each time, but he
stayed on the rock. He waited for the last lamb
to test his strength.

The youngster rushed up and pushed very
hard. Bighorn fell to his knees, but he kept his
place on the platform. He was the strongest
lamb in the group. After a few moments, he left
the rock with a wag of his tail and ran around in
circles.

The other lambs watched him, but not for

long. Their mothers were bleating that it was dinnertime. Through the grass and flowers the youngsters raced to get their meal.

Bighorn hurried to claim his. He nuzzled close to his mother and drank as fast as her milk came. When he finished nursing, he lay down and went to sleep.

His mother and the other ewes were eating plants in the meadow, but after a while they rested and chewed their cuds. These were small balls of undigested food that their stomach muscles had pushed up into their mouths. The ewes chewed and swallowed the cuds a second time to let them digest in the three other parts of their stomachs. Then the mothers dozed, and the oldest ewe went back to her post on a nearby ridge and stood guard.

Presently Bighorn woke up. His playmates were still sleeping, so he wandered to the edge of the meadow where a large sulphur butterfly attracted his attention. She was fanning her yellow and black wings on a shrub.

Bighorn dashed up and was about to sniff at the butterfly when she took off and flew to another bush.

Bighorn chased after her. He went from shrub to shrub until the sun made him so hot that he lay down in the shade of a boulder. Among the rocks and grass around him, Bighorn's sharp eyes soon saw something move. It was a white-tailed ptarmigan sitting on her nest on the ground. She was a grouse whose brown and white feathers blended in with her surroundings and made her look like a rock.

Bighorn got up to investigate, but the bird instantly flew off her nest. In it were seven cream-colored eggs mottled in brown.

Bighorn sniffed at the eggs and then turned and looked all around the area. His mother was nowhere in sight. He baaed loudly and ran across the open stretch of country, leaving the meadow behind him.

Soon he saw three wild sheep with large horns walking ahead. He scampered up to the rams.

They looked at him in silence and continued on their way.

Bighorn stood still and baaed at them.

By this time his mother had missed him in the meadow. Bleating loudly, she set out to find him. After she had gone a short distance, she stopped and listened for an answer.

Far away there was the cry of the golden eagle. It was followed by the howl of a coyote. After that all was silent except for the murmer of a stream close by.

The mother broke into a fast run and bleated again.

Bighorn heard her cries. He ran in the direction from which they had come, answering all the while.

Before long Bighorn was snuggling up close to his mother. As they started back to the meadow, he saw another butterfly, but he did not chase after it. Tired, he walked by his mother's side.

4

DOWN TO THE
SALT LICKS

It was summer. The sun shone warmly from a bright blue sky and melted big patches of snow on the Rocky Mountain peaks. The little meadows high up in the rugged country were filled with flowers. Bumblebees were busy gathering pollen, and large deer flies darted here and there.

Bighorn had grown fast since his baby days on the high ledge of the nursery. Two tiny horns were sprouting from his forehead, and he no longer took milk from his mother. Instead he ate grass and tender plants.

Frequently when the band traveled from one

spot to another in their search for food, Bighorn
would look down at the ranchers' sheep grazing
on the lower slopes and in the valley below. He
was not aware that they were eating grass and
plants and thus stripping the land of vegetation.
All he knew was that the rocky ledges far up in
the broken slopes were his home, and that the
bighorn lambs were his playmates.

One morning at mealtime Bighorn sniffed at
some grass and turned away from it. He was not
hungry, and neither was his mother or the rest
of the band. Because they craved salt the old
ewe set out for a clay bluff below timberline.
Mothers and lambs followed her across a stretch
of rocky ground.

Soon the old ewe climbed to a high point above
them, and the band waited while she looked for
danger. She saw nothing to alarm her. Besides,
a hoary marmot was watching on a ridge close
by. So the old ewe hurried back to the flock, and
they traveled over more rocky ground.

After a while they started down a cliff in a long

procession. They jumped from ledge to ledge on their cushioned feet. When they reached the bottom, they came to a pile of rocks that had been torn loose from the cliff by frost and heat. Several pikas were living in the rock slide.

The band drank some water from a pool nearby and then lay down to rest on the edge of the rock field. It was not long before Bighorn noticed a pika gathering bits of grass and plants and placing them on the rocks. The tiny rock rabbit was harvesting crops for the winter. Back and forth she went, collecting bundles of forage and drying them in the sun. After a while she sat on a food pile and looked over at Bighorn. He stared back and then got up to stretch his legs.

The band was ready to move on. They traveled over more rocky country, went down another cliff, and found themselves below timberline among some trees. They were out of the safety area now, and coyotes might be lurking in the underbrush. The old ewe stopped frequently to sniff the air and watch for danger. But presently she began walking at a fast pace. Straight ahead was the spot that she had visited many times for salt. It was a high bluff where many streaks of grayish clay were exposed. Here other wild sheep, deer, and mountain goats had also taken the salt.

Bighorn hurried up to the bluff. His tongue moved quickly as he licked the salt. It tasted so good that he wanted more. In a little while the lamb next to him had finished his meal of salt, but Bighorn kept on licking, his tail spinning like a top. Finally he left with the rest of the band to go back to the rugged country above timberline.

After they had gone a short distance, the old

ewe stopped and sniffed the air. She could not catch any danger scent, but she was not satisfied. Walking a few steps to the right, she looked anxiously in all directions. The mothers were also on the alert. Even the lambs seemed uneasy.

Suddenly a twig snapped in the stillness around them. A hungry coyote had found their tracks at the foot of the bluff and followed them.

Just then the old ewe caught sight of the coyote in the underbrush. Instantly she snorted a warning. The band broke into a wild run. In leaps and bounds they dashed across an open stretch, the lambs keeping up with their mothers.

Behind them came the coyote. Tail out straight, he rushed to catch up with the flock who were heading for a cliff — their one place of refuge.

The old ewe was in the lead. She reached the
foot of the giant wall and waited for the lambs to
climb to safety.

Bighorn and his mother arrived first. They
scampered up the cliff as nimbly as if they were
running on the ground. Next came the others

until there was only one mother and her lamb left. With several more feet to go, they were barely ahead of the coyote now. His body close to the ground, he lunged forward, ready to leap upon the youngster.

Quick as a whip the old ewe sprang into the air. Head lowered, she charged at the coyote. Her spiked horns struck him such a blow that he let out a loud yelp. He snapped at the old ewe with his powerful jaws, missing her by an inch. Then he cried out again, this time even louder. The hoofs of the mother ewe had torn into his back.

Defeated, the coyote scampered away. From a distance he watched the procession of wild sheep climbing higher and higher up the cliff.

42

5

FAMINE IN WINTER

Summer slipped into autumn. It was cold in the Rocky Mountains. The wind whistled and whined on the high slopes, and in the mornings everything was covered with frost.

The hoary marmot had gone to sleep for the winter, curled up in his underground den. But the pikas were running about, still collecting bundles of grass and plants to be stored in their rock slide.

One morning, when Bighorn awoke, he found snow falling. He got up and romped with the other youngsters in the big white flakes. He lapped up some to see how they tasted. Then, realizing he was hungry, he pawed for grass.

He soon found a patch because the snow was not deep. A few weeks later, though, his mother had to paw through eight inches of snow to reach some blades for him. Bighorn ate the frozen grass and then waited for his mother to paw away more snow.

In the afternoon a band of five rams came to mate with his mother and the other ewes. Bighorn watched the rams fight over the ewes; but he did not go near, since the battles terrified him.

As the weeks passed, rams kept coming and going, but some stayed with the band. The days were bitter cold now. Icy winds howled among the ridges and high snow-covered slopes. Like all the Rocky Mountain sheep Bighorn was dressed for the winter. He was wearing two coats — one of fine fur close to his skin and on top of that another of coarse hair. They kept him warm. But he was not able to find much to eat in his rugged home.

Years ago his ancestors had gone to the valleys in winter for food. That was before ranchers had shot many of them to protect the forage for their cattle. Now domestic sheep grazed on the lower slopes and meadows during most of the year and ate all the plants. So Bighorn and the wild sheep in the Rocky Mountains found winter a time of famine. Often the snow was so deep that they could not uncover grass and shrubs. As a result they frequently went to bed with empty stomachs.

One morning Bighorn was so hungry that he could not stop bleating. Everywhere he looked there was snow, since the wind had blown it into drifts during the night. However, there was one place where the snow was not deep, and some rams and ewes were trying to get through it.

Bighorn watched them, but he kept on bleating, his cries resounding pitifully in the still, cold air. The lamb next to him was silent. She had died of starvation before daybreak. Two other youngsters had died of disease a week before.

Finally the band made a trail in the snow. Bighorn and another lamb followed them in search

of food. They were the only youngsters left of
the five born last spring. As they walked slowly
along, a white-tailed ptarmigan flew low over
their heads. She was wearing her winter plum-
age. Her feathers were white — a perfect camou-
flage in the snow-covered world, and Bighorn's
sharp eyes saw the bird alight on a snowbank and
look as if she were part of it. He showed no
further interest in her, since he wanted something to eat. Instead he plodded along with the
others until they came to a spot where the wind
had blown away a lot of snow. It was near the
rock slide where the pikas lived, but they were
nowhere in sight.

Bighorn and his mother lost no time looking for their storehouses of food. Soon they found some bundles of dried grass and plants in the crevices of the rocks. They ate the food with relish. It helped to save their lives.

Then Bighorn hunted for more of the pikas' supplies, but they were buried too far down between the rocks for him to reach. So he joined his mother and the rest of the band as they nibbled on a few shrubs. The twigs satisfied them for a while.

The next morning they hunted again for food and found some shrubs on a wind-blown slope where the snow was shallow. But there was not enough for everyone in the band, so Bighorn's small breakfast did not fill his stomach. He was still hungry.

Day after day, all during the rest of the winter, Bighorn's meals were just enough to keep him from starving.

6

THE WHITE MONSTER

Spring finally came to the Rocky Mountains. The sun was warmer, and the wind no longer whistled and howled in the open country at the timberline.

Snow fleas leaped here and there and fed on the pollen of flowers blooming above the snow. Their wingless bodies looked like black dots against the white background.

The tracks of a horned lark marked a snow-bank. Her nest was close by, tucked in a bunch of grass. Not far from it Bighorn fed on some tender plants. He was thin from the rugged winter with so little food, but as the days went by he put on weight.

The rams who had been with his flock during the winter had gone off together in a band of their own. Bighorn did not seem to miss them. He was too busy eating grass and flowers that had sprung up in the little mountain meadows.

Presently his mother and the four ewes went to a high ledge to bear their new babies. Bighorn stayed with the yearling wild sheep and the old ewes. One afternoon as they were browsing near the top of a slope, a loud rumbling noise broke the stillness of the mountains.

Startled, Bighorn looked up. A huge mass of snow had broken loose from a high ridge and was rushing toward him. Bighorn turned and started across the slope at high speed. The old

ewe followed a few paces behind him. Next came
the yearling.

The white monster kept coming. It roared like
huge waves dashing against rocks. It rolled

51

faster and faster, picking up a boulder as big as an elephant.

Bighorn's heart pounded. He ran for his life, straining his legs to get out of the way of the snowslide. Fortunately he and the old ewe reached the edge of the slope in the nick of time. The yearling did not. The mass of snow fell on top of her. It carried her along—down, down, down, to the valley.

At the end of the day Bighorn followed the old ewe to a crest under a ridge. It was her favorite bedding ground, since here she could watch for danger. Bighorn watched her paw two old beds and make them smooth. Then he and the old ewe lay down and went to sleep.

The next morning they trotted to a meadow to feed. Bighorn kept looking up at the high ridges, ready to run in case there was another ball of moving snow. He was still uneasy when his mother came to the meadow with her new lamb. Then Bighorn seemed to forget everything else. He rushed up to the lamb to have some fun. His mother chased him away. She was afraid he would play too roughly with her youngster. Besides, Bighorn was old enough to take care of himself.

Later, when another ewe brought her lamb to the meadow, Bighorn tried again to have fun. This time the old ewe butted him with her spiked horns.

Bighorn did not fight back. He walked off by himself to look for a wild sheep his own age to romp with.

7

LOUD CRASHES

Many months went by. Bighorn was three and a half years old. He had reached the breeding age. His brown horns were curled like the older rams, only they were not as large.

The band that he had joined were all males, five of them including himself. All summer they had lived peaceably together, wandering about their home range for food.

Now that it was autumn, Bighorn was restless. He paced up and down an open area, jumped over some rocks, and climbed to the top of a ridge. Overhead a flock of geese flying in V formation were on their way south for the winter.

Bighorn watched the large birds until they

were out of sight. Then his attention turned to a wild goat standing on a rocky point. He was an excellent mountain climber, but he was stiff-gaited. Bighorn was agile. He could leap from ledge to ledge as if he were sailing on wings.

Soon the wild goat left his lookout, and Big-horn's keen eyes took in something else—ewes grazing in a high mountain meadow. He was not the only one to see the group. The ram with the largest horns had also seen the ewes.

It was not long before all five males were heading for the meadow. They hurried down a steep rugged slope, jumping from rock to rock on their cushioned feet. The large horned ram was in the lead, but Bighorn managed to reach the meadow a second after he did. With neck bulging and nose quivering, Bighorn strutted toward a female who was resting and chewing her cud.

She eyed him carefully. As he drew close she got up and dashed off, her white rump bouncing like a ball.

Bighorn chased after her, across the meadow

and around a big boulder. Finally he caught up with her. They stopped to get their breath when a young ram bounded up and struck Bighorn sideways with a sharp hoof.

Bighorn's eyes blazed. He rushed toward the intruder. Their horns crashed. They backed away and shook their heads in a daze. Then they rushed head-on again. Raising up on their hind legs, they brought their horns together in a fierce crash. The blow sent waves of shock through their bodies. After each charge, they stood quietly as if to let the stars clear from their heads.

For fifteen minutes Bighorn fought off the intruder. Finally he gave him such a blow with his horns that the young ram walked away.

Snorting proudly, Bighorn hurried to the ewe, who had been watching the fight. He had won his mate.

The next day Bighorn wanted to mate with a second ewe, and so did another ram. They fought over her and Bighorn lost. However, he was not discouraged. He charged at another male pursuing a female, and this time he won the battle. As he strutted over to the ewe, she broke into a fast run. Bighorn dashed after her, and soon they were scampering side by side.

The rest of the day more fights were waged between the rams for the ewes. Their large hollow horns crashed so loudly that the noise could have been heard a mile away. But Bighorn did not attack any more rams. Toward evening, when snow began to fall, he ate some grass and then went with the other wild sheep to a sheltered place for the night.

8

MAGNIFICENT HORNS

Years went by. It was fall again in the Rocky Mountains of Wyoming. Bighorn was almost eight years old. His horns were magnificent. They circled his head in one massive sweep. Unlike deer, who grow new antlers each summer, Bighorn kept his horns the year round.

He was standing on a high ridge now, looking down at the bluffs, ledges, and steep slopes of broken rock. Here in the rugged range of his home, coyotes were not likely to attack him. A mountain lion or a wolverine might wait in hiding for him among the cliffs, but there were so few of these animals left in the mountains that Bighorn had never seen one. His concern was the human hunter who killed wild sheep with guns.

Bighorn sniffed the air. Since it brought no scent of a gunner, he relaxed his vigil. His peace was not to last long, though. The figure of a man walking on a lower ridge caught his attention. Another good look, and he saw that he was carrying a gun.

Bighorn hurried to his band of four rams, who were resting in a meadow. He was their leader, so he cautiously led them farther away from the hunter. Then, while they grazed among rocks in an open space, Bighorn went to another ridge and looked out at the vast world before him. Satisfied that the gunner was not on their trail, he returned to his band and browsed with them.

The next morning the flock of wild sheep was up at sunrise. As they ate grass on a slope, Bighorn seemed uneasy again. He climbed to the top of the slope and gazed around anxiously. Suddenly he became tense. There, not too far away, was the hunter, and a short distance from him a mountain goat stood on a rocky ledge.

The man did not fire at the wild goat—his horns were only small black spikes. He was eager to kill a wild sheep because those horns would be a real prize in the world of sport.

Just then he saw Bighorn. His great curling horns would make a wonderful trophy. He raised his gun, aimed the sight carefully, and fired.

A loud shot rang out in the stillness. The bullet whizzed through the air and missed Bighorn by a hairsbreadth.

Terrified, he dashed down the slope. The rest of the band ran too, not realizing that another hunter lay hiding in a pile of rocks at the bottom. When he saw Bighorn, he fired immediately.

The bullet grazed Bighorn's side, doing little harm but making him run at full speed. He bounded across an open area, jumped over rocks and some brush.

At that moment two more shots rang out. Bighorn kept on running. He turned toward a steep, rugged cliff that ended in a bed of rocks a thousand feet below. There was no time to hesitate. Bighorn wheeled to the edge and jumped. Down, down, he sailed through the air until his cushioned feet struck a small ledge. He stood on the shelf a second; then, catching sight of another

rocky point, he leaped and landed with the same ease. From there he continued downward, bounding from one tiny ledge to another until he reached the bottom.

Safe now from the hunter, Bighorn lay down and rested among the rocks. After a short nap he went back to his band and grazed with them in a meadow, but he still kept on the lookout for danger.

As the days went by Bighorn's life became one of extreme caution, for there still were men hunting wild sheep in his mountains.

Not until the heavy snows set in did they depart. Bighorn could be less tense now, but he was always hungry. All during the cold months ahead, he found little to eat. Yet somehow he managed to survive the winter.

When spring came he was very thin, but fresh grass was showing between patches of snow on the high slopes. After Bighorn had eaten all he could find, he went to his favorite lookout on a rocky point. For almost fifteen minutes he stood there—a beautiful wild animal with magnificent horns. Then Bighorn watched the sun rise above the snow-capped peaks, not knowing when a shot would ring out in his rugged mountain home.

MARY ADRIAN

Miss Adrian graduated from Great Neck High School, Great Neck, Long Island, and studied at New York University. She was born in Sewickley, Pennsylvania. She is married to Henry Jorgensen and lives in Salem, Oregon.

Her literary record is an impressive one. She has had nature stories and articles published in *Boys' Life, Country Gentleman, Farm Journal, Jack and Jill. The Grade Teacher, Trails for Juniors* (Methodist Sunday School Paper) and *The Christian Science Monitor.* A nature column by her ran in the Sunday Magazine Section of the *Boston Post* for years, and she had a feature in *House Beautiful* called *Did You Know?* which dealt with unusual facts of nature.

Besides this she has published the following nature books: *Garden Spider, Honeybee, Fiddler Crab,* and *Gray Squirrel* (Holiday House), and many mystery stories based on nature information. See the complete list of her books opposite the title page.

The author and her husband are both members of the American Ornithologists Union, the National Audubon Society and the National Wildlife Federation.

GENEVIEVE VAUGHAN-JACKSON

Born in England, the artist spent the years from 1920 to 1926 in the west of Ireland in the depths of the country. This interlude was followed by school in England, after which there were two years of art school in Paris. She lived with a French family, and spent summers in the Alps with them, climbing and sketching.

In 1937, she came to the United States to teach art at the Foote School in New Haven where she enjoyed working with the children very much. During World War II she had a war job in the drafting room of a marine engineering company, and after that took up free-lance art work, finally landing in the field of children's books.

Her husband is John Shimer, professor of geology at Brooklyn College. They live in New York City.

Miss Vaughan-Jackson has written and illustrated two books of her own: *Animals and Men in Armor* and *Mountains of Fire, an Introduction to the Science of Volcanos.*

DATE DUE

5/16/69			
10/22/69			
1/21/70			
4/21/71			
1-29-72			
4-9-73			
2 5 74			
11/17/77			
12-1-77			
12-8-77			
4 25 94			